Other golf books by Exley:
Golf Quotations   The Fanatics Guide to Golf
Golf Jokes   Golf a Celebration
The Crazy World of Golf   The Golfer's Address Book

Published simultaneously in 1993 by Exley Publications in
Great Britain, and Exley Giftbooks in the USA.

BORDER ILLUSTRATIONS BY RUSSELL BARNETT

ISBN 1-85015-448-1

Edited and pictures selected by Helen Exley.
Designed by Pinpoint Design.
Picture research by P. A. Goldberg and J. M. Clift, Image Select,
London.
Typeset by Delta, Watford.
Printed and bound in Spain by Graficas Reunidas S.A., Madrid.

**Exley Publications Ltd, 16 Chalk Hill, Watford,
Herts WD1 4BN, United Kingdom.**

**Exley Giftbooks, 359 East Main Street, Suite 3D, Mt. Kisco,
NY 10549, USA.**

Golf

SCORE BOOK

EDITED BY
HELEN EXLEY

▨ EXLEY
MT. KISCO, NEW YORK • WATFORD, UK

CONTENTS

This book is carefully designed to help you to improve on, or polish up your game. Keep the Round Reports alongside your regular score cards - they will tell you more than just your score as compared with your partners'. By filling in details of your *own* performance you will be able to analyze your game and thereby establish strengths and weaknesses. You will be able to locate and tackle any flaws by tracing patterns in your scores. On the simplest level, for example, a good first nine compared to the second nine could mean you need more exercise. (And a tendency to poor scores on your first three holes could point to the need for some warm-up strokes before you start your game.)

IMPORTANT TELEPHONE NUMBERS

THIS BOOK BELONGS TO

ADDRESS

TEL HOME:

TEL WORK:

FAX:

GOLF PRO

TEL/FAX

GOLF SUPPLIES

TEL/FAX:

HOME COURSE

TEL:

FAX:

NAME

TEL/FAX:

NAME

TEL/FAX:

NAME

TEL/FAX:

NAME

TEL/FAX:

NAME

TEL/FAX:

NAME

TEL/FAX:

NAME

TEL/FAX:

NAME

TEL/FAX:

TELEPHONE NUMBERS: GOLF PARTNERS

NAME

ADDRESS

TEL HOME: TEL WORK:

FAX:

NAME

ADDRESS

TEL HOME: TEL WORK:

FAX:

NAME

ADDRESS

TEL HOME: TEL WORK:

FAX:

NAME

ADDRESS

TEL HOME: TEL WORK:

FAX:

TELEPHONE NUMBERS: GOLF PARTNERS

NAME

ADDRESS

TEL HOME: TEL WORK:

FAX:

NAME

ADDRESS

TEL HOME: TEL WORK:

FAX:

NAME

ADDRESS

TEL HOME: TEL WORK:

FAX:

NAME

ADDRESS

TEL HOME: TEL WORK:

FAX:

TELEPHONE NUMBERS: GOLF PARTNERS

NAME

ADDRESS

TEL HOME: TEL WORK:

FAX:

NAME

ADDRESS

TEL HOME: TEL WORK:

FAX:

NAME

ADDRESS

TEL HOME: TEL WORK:

FAX:

NAME

ADDRESS

TEL HOME: TEL WORK:

FAX:

TELEPHONE NUMBERS: GOLF PARTNERS

NAME

ADDRESS

TEL HOME: TEL WORK:

FAX:

NAME

ADDRESS

TEL HOME: TEL WORK:

FAX:

NAME

ADDRESS

TEL HOME: TEL WORK:

FAX:

NAME

ADDRESS

TEL HOME: TEL WORK:

FAX:

13

TELEPHONE NUMBERS: GOLF PARTNERS

NAME

ADDRESS

TEL HOME: TEL WORK:

FAX:

NAME

ADDRESS

TEL HOME: TEL WORK:

FAX:

NAME

ADDRESS

TEL HOME: TEL WORK:

FAX:

NAME

ADDRESS

TEL HOME: TEL WORK:

FAX:

TELEPHONE NUMBERS: GOLF PARTNERS

NAME

ADDRESS

TEL HOME: TEL WORK:

FAX:

NAME

ADDRESS

TEL HOME: TEL WORK:

FAX:

NAME

ADDRESS

TEL HOME: TEL WORK:

FAX:

NAME

ADDRESS

TEL HOME: TEL WORK:

FAX:

TELEPHONE NUMBERS: GOLF PARTNERS

NAME

ADDRESS

TEL HOME: TEL WORK:

FAX:

NAME

ADDRESS

TEL HOME: TEL WORK:

FAX:

NAME

ADDRESS

TEL HOME: TEL WORK:

FAX:

NAME

ADDRESS

TEL HOME: TEL WORK:

FAX:

TELEPHONE NUMBERS: GOLF PARTNERS

NAME

ADDRESS

TEL HOME: TEL WORK:

FAX:

NAME

ADDRESS

TEL HOME: TEL WORK:

FAX:

TELEPHONE NUMBERS: GOLF PARTNERS

NAME

ADDRESS

TEL HOME: TEL WORK:

FAX:

NAME

ADDRESS

TEL HOME: TEL WORK:

FAX:

BILOXI
GULFPORT
PASS
CHRISTIAN

TELEPHONE NUMBERS: GOLF PARTNERS

NAME

ADDRESS

TEL HOME: TEL WORK:

FAX:

NAME

ADDRESS

TEL HOME: TEL WORK:

FAX:

NAME

ADDRESS

TEL HOME: TEL WORK:

FAX:

NAME

ADDRESS

TEL HOME: TEL WORK:

FAX:

19

COURSE	
ADDRESS	
TEL:	
FAX:	
FEES	
BOOKING DETAILS	
PAR	
YARDAGE	
PRO	

Map your yardages on your course. Place a cross or sign on the map on features such as a prominent tree(s) or a bridge which will act as distance markers.

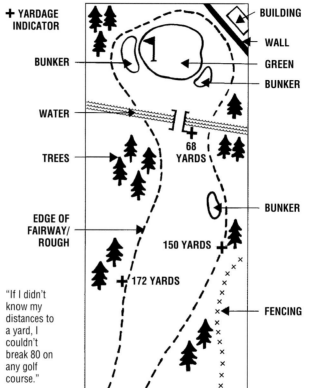

+ YARDAGE INDICATOR

BUNKER

WATER

TREES

EDGE OF FAIRWAY/ ROUGH

"If I didn't know my distances to a yard, I couldn't break 80 on any golf course."

BUILDING

WALL

GREEN

BUNKER

68 YARDS

BUNKER

150 YARDS

+172 YARDS

FENCING

1	PAR:

10	PAR:

2 PAR:	3 PAR:	4 PAR:	5 PAR:	6 PAR:	7 PAR:	8 PAR:	9 PAR:

11 PAR:	12 PAR:	13 PAR:	14 PAR:	15 PAR:	16 PAR:	17 PAR:	18 PAR:

Guide officiel

VILLARS, CHESIÈRES,

Altitude:
1300-1800 m **ARVEYES, BRETAYE** Ligne
du Simplon

La Perle des Stations de Montagne
de la Suisse Romande

LUCERNE
AND
CENTRAL SWITZERLAND

GOLF COURSES

COURSE	COURSE	COURSE
ADDRESS	ADDRESS	ADDRESS
TEL:	TEL:	TEL:
FAX:	FAX:	FAX:
FEES	FEES	FEES
BOOKING DETAILS	BOOKING DETAILS	BOOKING DETAILS
PAR	PAR	PAR
YARDAGE	YARDAGE	YARDAGE
PRO	PRO	PRO
COMMENTS	COMMENTS	COMMENTS

GOLF COURSES

COURSE	COURSE	COURSE
ADDRESS	ADDRESS	ADDRESS
TEL:	TEL:	TEL:
FAX:	FAX:	FAX:
FEES	FEES	FEES
BOOKING DETAILS	BOOKING DETAILS	BOOKING DETAILS
PAR	PAR	PAR
YARDAGE	YARDAGE	YARDAGE
PRO	PRO	PRO
COMMENTS	COMMENTS	COMMENTS

GOLF COURSES

COURSE	COURSE	COURSE
ADDRESS	ADDRESS	ADDRESS
TEL:	TEL:	TEL:
FAX:	FAX:	FAX:
FEES	FEES	FEES
BOOKING DETAILS	BOOKING DETAILS	BOOKING DETAILS
PAR	PAR	PAR
YARDAGE	YARDAGE	YARDAGE
PRO	PRO	PRO
COMMENTS	COMMENTS	COMMENTS

25

GOLF COURSES

COURSE	COURSE	COURSE
ADDRESS	ADDRESS	ADDRESS
TEL:	TEL:	TEL:
FAX:	FAX:	FAX:
FEES	FEES	FEES
BOOKING DETAILS	BOOKING DETAILS	BOOKING DETAILS
PAR	PAR	PAR
YARDAGE	YARDAGE	YARDAGE
PRO	PRO	PRO
COMMENTS	COMMENTS	COMMENTS

GOLF COURSES

COURSE	COURSE	COURSE
ADDRESS	ADDRESS	ADDRESS
TEL:	TEL:	TEL:
FAX:	FAX:	FAX:
FEES	FEES	FEES
BOOKING DETAILS	BOOKING DETAILS	BOOKING DETAILS
PAR	PAR	PAR
YARDAGE	YARDAGE	YARDAGE
PRO	PRO	PRO
COMMENTS	COMMENTS	COMMENTS

GOLF COURSES

COURSE	COURSE	COURSE
ADDRESS	ADDRESS	ADDRESS
TEL:	TEL:	TEL:
FAX:	FAX:	FAX:
FEES	FEES	FEES
BOOKING DETAILS	BOOKING DETAILS	BOOKING DETAILS
PAR	PAR	PAR
YARDAGE	YARDAGE	YARDAGE
PRO	PRO	PRO
COMMENTS	COMMENTS	COMMENTS

GOLF COURSES

COURSE	COURSE	COURSE
ADDRESS	ADDRESS	ADDRESS
TEL:	TEL:	TEL:
FAX:	FAX:	FAX:
FEES	FEES	FEES
BOOKING DETAILS	BOOKING DETAILS	BOOKING DETAILS
PAR	PAR	PAR
YARDAGE	YARDAGE	YARDAGE
PRO	PRO	PRO
COMMENTS	COMMENTS	COMMENTS

ROUND REPORT

COURSE									DATE				TIME START				FINISH			
HOLES	1	2	3	4	5	6	7	8	9	10	11	12	13	14	15	16	17	18	TOTAL	H	NETT FINISH
YARDAGE																					
PAR																					
SCORE																					
PARTNER																					
PARTNER																					
PARTNER																					
FAIRWAY																					
CHIIPSHOT																					
SANDSHOT																					
PUTT																					

NOTES: TYPE COMPETITION/WEATHER ETC.

ANALYSIS	FAIRWAY	CHIPSHOTS	SANDSHOTS	PUTTS	RESULT	
HOLES 1-9					W	L
HOLES 10-18					PAR	
TOTALS					NETT TOTAL	

ROUND REPORT

COURSE										DATE		TIME START					FINISH		
HOLES	1	2	3	4	5	6	7	8	9	10	11	12	13	14	15	16	17	18	TOTAL	H	NETT FINISH
YARDAGE																					
PAR																					
SCORE																					
PARTNER																					
PARTNER																					
PARTNER																					
FAIRWAY																					
CHIIPSHOT																					
SANDSHOT																					
PUTT																					

NOTES: TYPE COMPETITION/WEATHER ETC.

ANALYSIS	FAIRWAY	CHIPSHOTS	SANDSHOTS	PUTTS	RESULT	
HOLES 1-9					W	L
HOLES 10-18					PAR	
TOTALS					NETT TOTAL	

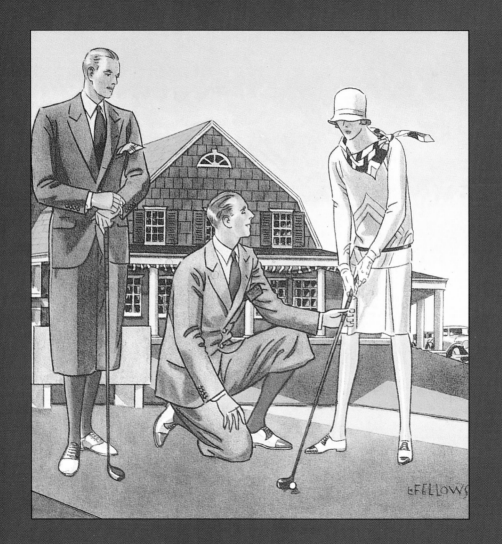

ROUND REPORT

COURSE										DATE				TIME START				FINISH		
HOLES	1	2	3	4	5	6	7	8	9	10	11	12	13	14	15	16	17	18	TOTAL	H	NETT FINISH
YARDAGE																					
PAR																					
SCORE																					
PARTNER																					
PARTNER																					
PARTNER																					
FAIRWAY																					
CHIIPSHOT																					
SANDSHOT																					
PUTT																					

NOTES: TYPE COMPETITION/WEATHER ETC.

ANALYSIS	FAIRWAY	CHIPSHOTS	SANDSHOTS	PUTTS	RESULT	
HOLES 1-9					W	L
HOLES 10-18					PAR	
TOTALS					NETT TOTAL	

35

GOLFING
IN SOUTHERN ENGLAND AND ON THE CONTINENT
PUBLISHED BY THE SOUTHERN RAILWAY

CHEMIN DE FER DU NORD
LE TOUQUET
Paris-Plage

GOLF: 45 Trous — TENNIS: 30 Courts
CHAMP DE COURSES — PLAGE DE SABLE
LA PLUS BELLE PISCINE D'EUROPE
66m66 de long sur 25m de large
Eau de mer réchauffée
CASINO DE LA PLAGE — CASINO DE LA FORÊT

ROUND REPORT

COURSE									DATE				TIME START				FINISH		
HOLES	1	2	3	4	5	6	7	8	9	10	11	12	13	14	15	16	17	18	TOTAL	H	NETT FINISH
YARDAGE																					
PAR																					
SCORE																					
PARTNER																					
PARTNER																					
PARTNER																					
FAIRWAY																					
CHIIPSHOT																					
SANDSHOT																					
PUTT																					

NOTES: TYPE COMPETITION/WEATHER ETC.

ANALYSIS	FAIRWAY	CHIPSHOTS	SANDSHOTS	PUTTS	RESULT	
HOLES 1-9					W	L
HOLES 10-18					PAR	
TOTALS					NETT TOTAL	

37

ROUND REPORT

COURSE									DATE				TIME START				FINISH		

HOLES	1	2	3	4	5	6	7	8	9	10	11	12	13	14	15	16	17	18	TOTAL	H	NETT FINISH
YARDAGE																					
PAR																					
SCORE																					
PARTNER																					
PARTNER																					
PARTNER																					
FAIRWAY																					
CHIIPSHOT																					
SANDSHOT																					
PUTT																					

NOTES: TYPE COMPETITION/WEATHER ETC.

ANALYSIS	FAIRWAY	CHIPSHOTS	SANDSHOTS	PUTTS	RESULT	
HOLES 1-9					W	L
HOLES 10-18					PAR	
TOTALS					NETT TOTAL	

ROUND REPORT

COURSE									DATE				TIME START				FINISH			
HOLES	1	2	3	4	5	6	7	8	9	10	11	12	13	14	15	16	17	18	TOTAL	H	NETT FINISH
YARDAGE																					
PAR																					
SCORE																					
PARTNER																					
PARTNER																					
PARTNER																					
FAIRWAY																					
CHIIPSHOT																					
SANDSHOT																					
PUTT																					

NOTES: TYPE COMPETITION/WEATHER ETC.

ANALYSIS	FAIRWAY	CHIPSHOTS	SANDSHOTS	PUTTS	RESULT	
HOLES 1-9					W	L
HOLES 10-18					PAR	
TOTALS					NETT TOTAL	

GOLF MONTE-CARLO

Affiches Photographiques ROBAUDY - CANNES

CRANS

SUR SIERRE · VALAIS · SUISSE 1500 M.s M.

GOLF ALPIN · PLAGE · TENNIS

ROUND REPORT

HOLES	1	2	3	4	5	6	7	8	9	10	11	12	13	14	15	16	17	18	TOTAL	H	NETT FINISH
COURSE							DATE						TIME START				FINISH			
YARDAGE																					
PAR																					
SCORE																					
PARTNER																					
PARTNER																					
PARTNER																					
FAIRWAY																					
CHIIPSHOT																					
SANDSHOT																					
PUTT																					

NOTES: TYPE COMPETITION/WEATHER ETC.

ANALYSIS	FAIRWAY	CHIPSHOTS	SANDSHOTS	PUTTS	RESULT	
HOLES 1-9					W	L
HOLES 10-18					PAR	
TOTALS					NETT TOTAL	

42

ROUND REPORT

COURSE										DATE				TIME START				FINISH			

HOLES	1	2	3	4	5	6	7	8	9	10	11	12	13	14	15	16	17	18	TOTAL	H	NETT FINISH
YARDAGE																					
PAR																					
SCORE																					
PARTNER																					
PARTNER																					
PARTNER																					
FAIRWAY																					
CHIIPSHOT																					
SANDSHOT																					
PUTT																					

NOTES: TYPE COMPETITION/WEATHER ETC.

ANALYSIS	FAIRWAY	CHIPSHOTS	SANDSHOTS	PUTTS	RESULT	
HOLES 1-9					W	L
HOLES 10-18					PAR	
TOTALS					NETT TOTAL	

ROUND REPORT

COURSE   DATE   TIME START   FINISH

HOLES	1	2	3	4	5	6	7	8	9	10	11	12	13	14	15	16	17	18	TOTAL	H	NETT FINISH
YARDAGE																					
PAR																					
SCORE																					
PARTNER																					
PARTNER																					
PARTNER																					
FAIRWAY																					
CHIIPSHOT																					
SANDSHOT																					
PUTT																					

NOTES: TYPE COMPETITION/WEATHER ETC.

ANALYSIS	FAIRWAY	CHIPSHOTS	SANDSHOTS	PUTTS	RESULT	
HOLES 1-9					W	L
HOLES 10-18					PAR	
TOTALS					NETT TOTAL	

ROUND REPORT

COURSE									DATE				TIME START				FINISH			
HOLES	1	2	3	4	5	6	7	8	9	10	11	12	13	14	15	16	17	18	TOTAL	H	NETT FINISH
YARDAGE																					
PAR																					
SCORE																					
PARTNER																					
PARTNER																					
PARTNER																					
FAIRWAY																					
CHIIPSHOT																					
SANDSHOT																					
PUTT																					

NOTES: TYPE COMPETITION/WEATHER ETC.

ANALYSIS	FAIRWAY	CHIPSHOTS	SANDSHOTS	PUTTS	RESULT	
HOLES 1-9					W	L
HOLES 10-18					PAR	
TOTALS					NETT TOTAL	

THE SATURDAY EVENING POST

An Illustrated Weekly
Founded A.D. 1728 by Benj. Franklin

Volume 197, Number 49

5 cents

JUNE 6, 1925

Thomas McMorrow—Henry C. Rowland—Richard Connell—Sewell Ford
John P. Marquand—George Pattullo—Ernest Fuhr—William R. Green, M.C.

golf de haute montagne

FONT-ROMEU

ALTITUDE 1800 m

HARPER'S

APRIL '98

ROUND REPORT

COURSE									DATE				TIME START				FINISH			

HOLES	1	2	3	4	5	6	7	8	9	10	11	12	13	14	15	16	17	18	TOTAL	H	NETT FINISH
YARDAGE																					
PAR																					
SCORE																					
PARTNER																					
PARTNER																					
PARTNER																					
FAIRWAY																					
CHIIPSHOT																					
SANDSHOT																					
PUTT																					

NOTES: TYPE COMPETITION/WEATHER ETC.

ANALYSIS	FAIRWAY	CHIPSHOTS	SANDSHOTS	PUTTS	RESULT	
HOLES 1-9					W	L
HOLES 10-18					PAR	
TOTALS					NETT TOTAL	

ROUND REPORT

COURSE										DATE				TIME START				FINISH			

HOLES	1	2	3	4	5	6	7	8	9	10	11	12	13	14	15	16	17	18	TOTAL	H	NETT FINISH
YARDAGE																					
PAR																					
SCORE																					
PARTNER																					
PARTNER																					
PARTNER																					
FAIRWAY																					
CHIIPSHOT																					
SANDSHOT																					
PUTT																					

NOTES: TYPE COMPETITION/WEATHER ETC.

ANALYSIS	FAIRWAY	CHIPSHOTS	SANDSHOTS	PUTTS	RESULT	
HOLES 1-9					W	L
HOLES 10-18					PAR	
TOTALS					NETT TOTAL	

ROUND REPORT

COURSE										DATE				TIME START				FINISH		

HOLES	1	2	3	4	5	6	7	8	9	10	11	12	13	14	15	16	17	18	TOTAL	H	NETT FINISH
YARDAGE																					
PAR																					
SCORE																					
PARTNER																					
PARTNER																					
PARTNER																					
FAIRWAY																					
CHIIPSHOT																					
SANDSHOT																					
PUTT																					

NOTES: TYPE COMPETITION/WEATHER ETC.

ANALYSIS	FAIRWAY	CHIPSHOTS	SANDSHOTS	PUTTS	RESULT	
HOLES 1-9					W	L
HOLES 10-18					PAR	
TOTALS					NETT TOTAL	

ROUND REPORT

COURSE										DATE				TIME START				FINISH			
HOLES	1	2	3	4	5	6	7	8	9	10	11	12	13	14	15	16	17	18	TOTAL	H	NETT FINISH
YARDAGE																					
PAR																					
SCORE																					
PARTNER																					
PARTNER																					
PARTNER																					
FAIRWAY																					
CHIIPSHOT																					
SANDSHOT																					
PUTT																					

NOTES: TYPE COMPETITION/WEATHER ETC.

ANALYSIS	FAIRWAY	CHIPSHOTS	SANDSHOTS	PUTTS	RESULT	
HOLES 1-9					W	L
HOLES 10-18					PAR	
TOTALS					NETT TOTAL	

ROUND REPORT

COURSE										DATE				TIME START				FINISH		

HOLES	1	2	3	4	5	6	7	8	9	10	11	12	13	14	15	16	17	18	TOTAL	H	NETT FINISH
YARDAGE																					
PAR																					
SCORE																					
PARTNER																					
PARTNER																					
PARTNER																					
FAIRWAY																					
CHIIPSHOT																					
SANDSHOT																					
PUTT																					

NOTES: TYPE COMPETITION/WEATHER ETC.

ANALYSIS	FAIRWAY	CHIPSHOTS	SANDSHOTS	PUTTS	RESULT	
HOLES 1-9					W	L
HOLES 10-18					PAR	
TOTALS					NETT TOTAL	

55

ROUND REPORT

COURSE									DATE				TIME START				FINISH			

HOLES	1	2	3	4	5	6	7	8	9	10	11	12	13	14	15	16	17	18	TOTAL	H	NETT FINISH
YARDAGE																					
PAR																					
SCORE																					
PARTNER																					
PARTNER																					
PARTNER																					
FAIRWAY																					
CHIIPSHOT																					
SANDSHOT																					
PUTT																					

NOTES: TYPE COMPETITION/WEATHER ETC.

ANALYSIS	FAIRWAY	CHIPSHOTS	SANDSHOTS	PUTTS	RESULT	
HOLES 1-9					W	L
HOLES 10-18					PAR	
TOTALS					NETT TOTAL	

57

ROUND REPORT

COURSE										DATE				TIME START				FINISH			
HOLES	1	2	3	4	5	6	7	8	9	10	11	12	13	14	15	16	17	18	TOTAL	H	NETT FINISH
YARDAGE																					
PAR																					
SCORE																					
PARTNER																					
PARTNER																					
PARTNER																					
FAIRWAY																					
CHIIPSHOT																					
SANDSHOT																					
PUTT																					

NOTES: TYPE COMPETITION/WEATHER ETC.

ANALYSIS	FAIRWAY	CHIPSHOTS	SANDSHOTS	PUTTS	RESULT	
HOLES 1-9					W	L
HOLES 10-18					PAR	
TOTALS					NETT TOTAL	

ROUND REPORT

COURSE										DATE				TIME START				FINISH		
HOLES	1	2	3	4	5	6	7	8	9	10	11	12	13	14	15	16	17	18	TOTAL	H	NETT FINISH
YARDAGE																					
PAR																					
SCORE																					
PARTNER																					
PARTNER																					
PARTNER																					
FAIRWAY																					
CHIIPSHOT																					
SANDSHOT																					
PUTT																					

NOTES: TYPE COMPETITION/WEATHER ETC.

ANALYSIS	FAIRWAY	CHIPSHOTS	SANDSHOTS	PUTTS	RESULT	
HOLES 1-9					W	L
HOLES 10-18					PAR	
TOTALS					NETT TOTAL	

ROUND REPORT

COURSE									DATE				TIME START			FINISH				

HOLES	1	2	3	4	5	6	7	8	9	10	11	12	13	14	15	16	17	18	TOTAL	H	NETT FINISH
YARDAGE																					
PAR																					
SCORE																					
PARTNER																					
PARTNER																					
PARTNER																					
FAIRWAY																					
CHIIPSHOT																					
SANDSHOT																					
PUTT																					

NOTES: TYPE COMPETITION/WEATHER ETC.

ANALYSIS	FAIRWAY	CHIPSHOTS	SANDSHOTS	PUTTS	RESULT	
HOLES 1-9					W	L
HOLES 10-18					PAR	
TOTALS					NETT TOTAL	

ROUND REPORT

COURSE										DATE			TIME START				FINISH			

HOLES	1	2	3	4	5	6	7	8	9	10	11	12	13	14	15	16	17	18	TOTAL	H	NETT FINISH
YARDAGE																					
PAR																					
SCORE																					
PARTNER																					
PARTNER																					
PARTNER																					
FAIRWAY																					
CHIIPSHOT																					
SANDSHOT																					
PUTT																					

NOTES: TYPE COMPETITION/WEATHER ETC.

ANALYSIS	FAIRWAY	CHIPSHOTS	SANDSHOTS	PUTTS	RESULT	
HOLES 1-9					W	L
HOLES 10-18					PAR	
TOTALS					NETT TOTAL	

ROUND REPORT

COURSE									DATE					TIME START				FINISH		

HOLES	1	2	3	4	5	6	7	8	9	10	11	12	13	14	15	16	17	18	TOTAL	H	NETT FINISH
YARDAGE																					
PAR																					
SCORE																					
PARTNER																					
PARTNER																					
PARTNER																					
FAIRWAY																					
CHIIPSHOT																					
SANDSHOT																					
PUTT																					

NOTES: TYPE COMPETITION/WEATHER ETC.

ANALYSIS	FAIRWAY	CHIPSHOTS	SANDSHOTS	PUTTS	RESULT	
HOLES 1-9					W	L
HOLES 10-18					PAR	
TOTALS					NETT TOTAL	

ROUND REPORT

COURSE									DATE				TIME START				FINISH			
HOLES	1	2	3	4	5	6	7	8	9	10	11	12	13	14	15	16	17	18	TOTAL	H	NETT FINISH
YARDAGE																					
PAR																					
SCORE																					
PARTNER																					
PARTNER																					
PARTNER																					
FAIRWAY																					
CHIIPSHOT																					
SANDSHOT																					
PUTT																					

NOTES: TYPE COMPETITION/WEATHER ETC.

ANALYSIS	FAIRWAY	CHIPSHOTS	SANDSHOTS	PUTTS	RESULT	
HOLES 1-9					W	L
HOLES 10-18					PAR	
TOTALS					NETT TOTAL	

65

ROUND REPORT

COURSE										DATE				TIME START				FINISH			

HOLES	1	2	3	4	5	6	7	8	9	10	11	12	13	14	15	16	17	18	TOTAL	H	NETT FINISH
YARDAGE																					
PAR																					
SCORE																					
PARTNER																					
PARTNER																					
PARTNER																					
FAIRWAY																					
CHIIPSHOT																					
SANDSHOT																					
PUTT																					

NOTES: TYPE COMPETITION/WEATHER ETC.

ANALYSIS	FAIRWAY	CHIPSHOTS	SANDSHOTS	PUTTS	RESULT	
HOLES 1-9					W	L
HOLES 10-18					PAR	
TOTALS					NETT TOTAL	

ROUND REPORT

COURSE									DATE				TIME START				FINISH			

HOLES	1	2	3	4	5	6	7	8	9	10	11	12	13	14	15	16	17	18	TOTAL	H	NETT FINISH
YARDAGE																					
PAR																					
SCORE																					
PARTNER																					
PARTNER																					
PARTNER																					
FAIRWAY																					
CHIIPSHOT																					
SANDSHOT																					
PUTT																					

NOTES: TYPE COMPETITION/WEATHER ETC.

ANALYSIS	FAIRWAY	CHIPSHOTS	SANDSHOTS	PUTTS	RESULT	
HOLES 1-9					W	L
HOLES 10-18					PAR	
TOTALS					NETT TOTAL	

ROUND REPORT

COURSE										DATE				TIME START				FINISH		

HOLES	1	2	3	4	5	6	7	8	9	10	11	12	13	14	15	16	17	18	TOTAL	H	NETT FINISH
YARDAGE																					
PAR																					
SCORE																					
PARTNER																					
PARTNER																					
PARTNER																					
FAIRWAY																					
CHIIPSHOT																					
SANDSHOT																					
PUTT																					

NOTES: TYPE COMPETITION/WEATHER ETC.

ANALYSIS	FAIRWAY	CHIPSHOTS	SANDSHOTS	PUTTS	RESULT	
HOLES 1-9					W	L
HOLES 10-18					PAR	
TOTALS					NETT TOTAL	

68

ROUND REPORT

COURSE										DATE					TIME START				FINISH		
HOLES	1	2	3	4	5	6	7	8	9	10	11	12	13	14	15	16	17	18	TOTAL	H	NETT FINISH
YARDAGE																					
PAR																					
SCORE																					
PARTNER																					
PARTNER																					
PARTNER																					
FAIRWAY																					
CHIIPSHOT																					
SANDSHOT																					
PUTT																					

NOTES: TYPE COMPETITION/WEATHER ETC.

ANALYSIS	FAIRWAY	CHIPSHOTS	SANDSHOTS	PUTTS	RESULT	
HOLES 1-9					W	L
HOLES 10-18					PAR	
TOTALS					NETT TOTAL	

April 21 1927

Life
·SPORTS NUMBER·

Price 15 cents

The Sport of Missing Men

LES GOLFS
de la Côte Basque
et du Béarn

COURSE										DATE					TIME START				FINISH		
HOLES	1	2	3	4	5	6	7	8	9	10	11	12	13	14	15	16	17	18	TOTAL	H	NETT FINISH
YARDAGE																					
PAR																					
SCORE																					
PARTNER																					
PARTNER																					
PARTNER																					
FAIRWAY																					
CHIIPSHOT																					
SANDSHOT																					
PUTT																					

NOTES: TYPE COMPETITION/WEATHER ETC.

ANALYSIS	FAIRWAY	CHIPSHOTS	SANDSHOTS	PUTTS	RESULT	
HOLES 1-9					W	L
HOLES 10-18					PAR	
TOTALS					NETT TOTAL	

72

ROUND REPORT

COURSE										DATE				TIME START				FINISH			
HOLES	1	2	3	4	5	6	7	8	9	10	11	12	13	14	15	16	17	18	TOTAL	H	NETT FINISH
YARDAGE																					
PAR																					
SCORE																					
PARTNER																					
PARTNER																					
PARTNER																					
FAIRWAY																					
CHIIPSHOT																					
SANDSHOT																					
PUTT																					

NOTES: TYPE COMPETITION/WEATHER ETC.

ANALYSIS	FAIRWAY	CHIPSHOTS	SANDSHOTS	PUTTS	RESULT	
HOLES 1-9					W	L
HOLES 10-18					PAR	
TOTALS					NETT TOTAL	

ROUND REPORT

COURSE								DATE			TIME START				FINISH				

HOLES	1	2	3	4	5	6	7	8	9	10	11	12	13	14	15	16	17	18	TOTAL	H	NETT FINISH
YARDAGE																					
PAR																					
SCORE																					
PARTNER																					
PARTNER																					
PARTNER																					
FAIRWAY																					
CHIIPSHOT																					
SANDSHOT																					
PUTT																					

NOTES: TYPE COMPETITION/WEATHER ETC.

ANALYSIS	FAIRWAY	CHIPSHOTS	SANDSHOTS	PUTTS	RESULT	
HOLES 1-9					W	L
HOLES 10-18					PAR	
TOTALS					NETT TOTAL	

ROUND REPORT

COURSE _____ DATE _____ TIME START _____ FINISH _____

HOLES	1	2	3	4	5	6	7	8	9	10	11	12	13	14	15	16	17	18	TOTAL	H	NETT FINISH
YARDAGE																					
PAR																					
SCORE																					
PARTNER																					
PARTNER																					
PARTNER																					
FAIRWAY																					
CHIIPSHOT																					
SANDSHOT																					
PUTT																					

NOTES: TYPE COMPETITION/WEATHER ETC.

ANALYSIS	FAIRWAY	CHIPSHOTS	SANDSHOTS	PUTTS	RESULT	
HOLES 1-9					W	L
HOLES 10-18					PAR	
TOTALS					NETT TOTAL	

77

ROUND REPORT

COURSE										DATE				TIME START				FINISH			
HOLES	1	2	3	4	5	6	7	8	9	10	11	12	13	14	15	16	17	18	TOTAL	H	NETT FINISH
YARDAGE																					
PAR																					
SCORE																					
PARTNER																					
PARTNER																					
PARTNER																					
FAIRWAY																					
CHIIPSHOT																					
SANDSHOT																					
PUTT																					

NOTES: TYPE COMPETITION/WEATHER ETC.

ANALYSIS	FAIRWAY	CHIPSHOTS	SANDSHOTS	PUTTS	RESULT	
HOLES 1-9					W	L
HOLES 10-18					PAR	
TOTALS					NETT TOTAL	

ROUND REPORT

COURSE										DATE				TIME START				FINISH			
HOLES	1	2	3	4	5	6	7	8	9	10	11	12	13	14	15	16	17	18	TOTAL	H	NETT FINISH
YARDAGE																					
PAR																					
SCORE																					
PARTNER																					
PARTNER																					
PARTNER																					
FAIRWAY																					
CHIIPSHOT																					
SANDSHOT																					
PUTT																					

NOTES: TYPE COMPETITION/WEATHER ETC.

ANALYSIS	FAIRWAY	CHIPSHOTS	SANDSHOTS	PUTTS	RESULT	
HOLES 1-9					W	L
HOLES 10-18					PAR	
TOTALS					NETT TOTAL	

ROUND REPORT

COURSE									DATE				TIME START			FINISH			

HOLES	1	2	3	4	5	6	7	8	9	10	11	12	13	14	15	16	17	18	TOTAL	H	NETT FINISH
YARDAGE																					
PAR																					
SCORE																					
PARTNER																					
PARTNER																					
PARTNER																					
FAIRWAY																					
CHIIPSHOT																					
SANDSHOT																					

NOTES: TYPE COMPETITION/WEATHER ETC.

ANALYSIS	FAIRWAY	CHIPSHOTS	SANDSHOTS	PUTTS	RESULT	
HOLES 1-9					W	L
HOLES 10-18					PAR	
TOTALS					NETT TOTAL	

VICHY
SES SOURCES

SPORTS TOURISME THEATRE

ALTITUDE
1800m

GOLF DE HAUTE MONTAGNE
FONT-ROMEU

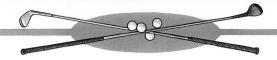

COURSE										DATE					TIME START			FINISH			
HOLES	1	2	3	4	5	6	7	8	9	10	11	12	13	14	15	16	17	18	TOTAL	H	NETT FINISH
YARDAGE																					
PAR																					
SCORE																					
PARTNER																					
PARTNER																					
PARTNER																					
FAIRWAY																					
CHIIPSHOT																					
SANDSHOT																					
PUTT																					

NOTES. TYPE COMPETITION/WEATHER ETC.

ANALYSIS	FAIRWAY	CHIPSHOTS	SANDSHOTS	PUTTS	RESULT	
HOLES 1-9					W	L
HOLES 10-18					PAR	
TOTALS					NETT TOTAL	

83

ROUND REPORT

COURSE										DATE				TIME START				FINISH		

HOLES	1	2	3	4	5	6	7	8	9	10	11	12	13	14	15	16	17	18	TOTAL	H	NETT FINISH
YARDAGE																					
PAR																					
SCORE																					
PARTNER																					
PARTNER																					
PARTNER																					
FAIRWAY																					
CHIIPSHOT																					
SANDSHOT																					
PUTT																					

NOTES: TYPE COMPETITION/WEATHER ETC.

ANALYSIS	FAIRWAY	CHIPSHOTS	SANDSHOTS	PUTTS	RESULT	
HOLES 1-9					W	L
HOLES 10-18					PAR	
TOTALS					NETT TOTAL	

ROUND REPORT

COURSE										DATE				TIME START				FINISH			

HOLES	1	2	3	4	5	6	7	8	9	10	11	12	13	14	15	16	17	18	TOTAL	H	NETT FINISH
YARDAGE																					
PAR																					
SCORE																					
PARTNER																					
PARTNER																					
PARTNER																					
FAIRWAY																					
CHIIPSHOT																					
SANDSHOT																					
PUTT																					

NOTES: TYPE COMPETITION/WEATHER ETC.

ANALYSIS	FAIRWAY	CHIPSHOTS	SANDSHOTS	PUTTS	RESULT	
HOLES 1-9					W	L
HOLES 10-18					PAR	
TOTALS					NETT TOTAL	

ROUND REPORT

COURSE										DATE		TIME START				FINISH				
HOLES	1	2	3	4	5	6	7	8	9	10	11	12	13	14	15	16	17	18	TOTAL	H	NETT FINISH
YARDAGE																					
PAR																					
SCORE																					
PARTNER																					
PARTNER																					
PARTNER																					
FAIRWAY																					
CHIIPSHOT																					
SANDSHOT																					
PUTT																					

NOTES: TYPE COMPETITION/WEATHER ETC.

ANALYSIS	FAIRWAY	CHIPSHOTS	SANDSHOTS	PUTTS	RESULT	
HOLES 1-9					W	L
HOLES 10-18					PAR	
TOTALS					NETT TOTAL	

ROUND REPORT

COURSE   DATE   TIME START   FINISH

HOLES	1	2	3	4	5	6	7	8	9	10	11	12	13	14	15	16	17	18	TOTAL	H	NETT FINISH
YARDAGE																					
PAR																					
SCORE																					
PARTNER																					
PARTNER																					
PARTNER																					
FAIRWAY																					
CHIIPSHOT																					
SANDSHOT																					
PUTT																					

NOTES: TYPE COMPETITION/WEATHER ETC.

ANALYSIS	FAIRWAY	CHIPSHOTS	SANDSHOTS	PUTTS	RESULT	
HOLES 1-9					W	L
HOLES 10-18					PAR	
TOTALS					NETT TOTAL	

89

ROUND REPORT

COURSE									DATE				TIME START				FINISH			
HOLES	1	2	3	4	5	6	7	8	9	10	11	12	13	14	15	16	17	18	TOTAL	H	NETT FINISH
YARDAGE																					
PAR																					
SCORE																					
PARTNER																					
PARTNER																					
PARTNER																					
FAIRWAY																					
CHIIPSHOT																					
SANDSHOT																					
PUTT																					

NOTES: TYPE COMPETITION/WEATHER ETC.

ANALYSIS	FAIRWAY	CHIPSHOTS	SANDSHOTS	PUTTS	RESULT	
HOLES 1-9					W	L
HOLES 10-18					PAR	
TOTALS					NETT TOTAL	

ACKNOWLEDGEMENTS

The Publishers wish to thank Rosenstiel's Widow and Son Ltd. and The Burlington Gallery for their help in providing pictures for this book.

COVER NICK BIRCH/EXLEY PUBLICATIONS.

TITLE PAGE NICK BIRCH/EXLEY PUBLICATIONS.

PAGE 6 PETER FIORE, The Image Bank.

PAGE 9 PORTRAIT OF A WOMAN GOLFER MAUDE MARTIN ELLIS, Private Collection, The Bridgeman Art Library.

PAGE 17 SOURCE UNKNOWN.

PAGE 18 SARAH FABIAN BADDIEL, Golfiana, Grays in the Mews B10, Davies Mews, London W1. Tel: 071 408 1239.

PAGE 22 a. NICK BIRCH/EXLEY PUBLICATIONS, b. NICK BIRCH/EXLEY PUBLICATIONS.

PAGE 30 SARAH FABIAN BADDIEL.

PAGE 32 GOLF IN ITALY MAX MINON, The Bridgeman Art Library.

PAGE 34 SARAH FABIAN BADDIEL.

PAGE 36 a. GOLFING – IN SOUTHERN ENGLAND AND THE CONTINENT, ARTIST UNKNOWN, Private Collection, The Bridgeman Art Library. b. CHEMIN DE FER DU NORD, E. COURCHINOUX, Private Collection, Paris.

PAGE 38 GOLFER DRIVING BALL OUT OF SAND TRAP, BONNOT, The Image Bank.

PAGE 41 a. NICK BIRCH/EXLEY PUBLICATIONS. b. MARTIN PEIKERT.

PAGE 43 NICK BIRCH/EXLEY PUBLICATIONS.

PAGE 47 THE SATURDAY EVENING POST, JUNE 6 1925, The Advertising Archive.

PAGE 48 a. GOLF DE HAUTE MONTAGNE, Explorer Archives. b. GOLFER AT TEE-OFF, Lords Gallery, London, The Bridgeman Art Library.

PAGE 51 SOURCE UNKNOWN.

PAGE 53 THE SATURDAY EVENING POST, SEPTEMBER 12 1931, The Advertising Archive.

PAGE 56 NICK BIRCH/EXLEY PUBLICATIONS.

PAGE 63 A TOUR IN ITALY ROMAN CAMPAGNA, WITH GOLFERS, EDINA-VITORIO ACCORNESRO, Private Collection, The Bridgeman Art Library.

PAGE 64 SARAH FABIAN BADDIEL.

PAGE 69 SARAH FABIAN BADDIEL.

PAGE 71 NICK BIRCH/EXLEY PUBLICATIONS.

PAGE 73 PLAYING GOLF, MICHAEL SCHWAB, The Image Bank.

PAGE 74 SOURCE UNKNOWN.

PAGE 79 SARAH FABIAN BADDIEL.

PAGE 82 a. SARAH FABIAN BADDIEL. b. SARAH FABIAN BADDIEL.

PAGE 84 SARAH FABIAN BADDIEL.

PAGE 88 GOLFER'S FEET AND CLUB MISSING TEE-OFF, MOIRA MAHN, The Image Bank.

PAGE 91 THE BRITISH OPEN (c. 1920).